Expressing His Life

Life and relationships in God's Family

Study Manual

A course for group study developed by members of Post Green Community, edited by Jeanne Hinton.

A leaders' pack sold separately contains one study manual, two leaders' handbooks and a cassette.

Celebration Publishing
57 Dorchester Road, Lytchett Minster, Poole,
Dorset BH16 6JE, United Kingdom

ACKNOWLEDGMENTS

We are grateful to Collins Publishers for their permission to quote from J.B. Phillips' *The Young Church in Action* and to Coverdale House Publishers for permission to quote from *The Living Bible.* Other scripture references are from the Revised Standard Version of the Bible, copyrighted 1946, 1952, © 1971, 1973 .

The illustrations in this manual are by Alison Brown.

 First published 1975. This edition 1978. ISBN 0 906309 04 2. Printed in Great Britain for Celebration Services (Post Green) Ltd., 57 Dorchester Road, Lytchett Minster, Poole, Dorset BH16 6JE, by Friary Press Ltd., Friary Lane, Dorchester, Dorset.

PREFACE

This course was first printed in 1975 and now appears in a revised form with a new Leaders' Handbook and cassette.

In the first instance, the course was developed by Post Green for use in a Norfolk parish. Before its first printing, it was then tested out in a number of different churches, including a working class parish in the North of England, a fashionable church in the centre of London and two churches in rural areas of Norfolk. The draft material was then re-worked on the basis of their evaluations and suggestions.

Post Green is a community in Dorset made up of families and single people, ordained and lay, of different denominations. The community is one of a fellowship of congregations and communities who have discovered a radically new life-style and are experimenting with new forms of corporate life and leadership. These congregations/communities in the U.K., U.S.A. and in other countries have a common concern for the renewal of the church and of society. The story of Post Green Community is told in *Love is Our Home* by Faith Lees with Jeanne Hinton, a Hodder paperback, published 1978.

CONTENTS

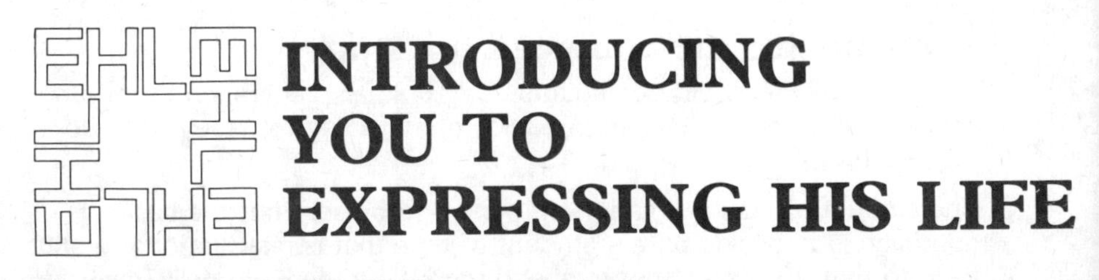

INTRODUCING YOU TO EXPRESSING HIS LIFE

Life and Relationships in God's family

About the course

Expressing His Life aims to help participants understand more clearly what the Christian life is all about and to experience belonging to a group of people whose desire it is to live out the life of Christ in their local situation.

It is a course for group study. A Leaders' pack sold separately contains study manual, cassette and leaders' handbooks. The handbook gives full instructions for running the course.

How long it takes

There are six sections; each section divided into four separate studies. The course, therefore, takes approximately six months, if one study is completed per week.

What you have to do

The six sections cover New Life in Christ, the Holy Spirit, Gifts of the Spirit, Serving Together, Living Together and Expressing the Life of Christ.

The weekly studies are completed as preparation for group sharing. Space is allowed in this manual for written work.

As the course progresses the type of study varies. The first three sections seek, in particular, to help you study the bible and several different methods of personal bible study are introduced. In the last three sections there are fewer study questions, the emphasis being more on group sharing and on encouraging you to widen your knowledge by reading and listening to tapes.

Each weekly study contains one question to encourage more in depth study. You may not wish to complete this question or may decide to do so at a later date. However, if possible, complete it as part of your regular weekly study programme.

How much time you need for study

One hour a week could be enough study time as preparation for group sharing; some might want to put aside one evening for study or to do a little each day.

The amount of time will vary from person to person, but the best approach is to decide on the amount of time that is realistic for you and keep to that. Don't attempt to spend more time than you really have available or you will soon give up and do no preparation!

What else you need

For study purposes use a standard version of the bible, either the Authorised or Revised Standard Version. It will, however, help if you have other modern translations or paraphrases you can refer to as well. You will also need a bible concordance (you can buy a paperback concordance quite cheaply) and to be able, if possible, to refer to some good commentaries.

Don't, however, go out and purchase any of these aids until you have first met together with others doing the course. Your course co-ordinator will advise you about books available for reference purposes and give suggestions about others you might like to buy for your personal use.

As well as the study manual, you will probably need a notebook to make rough notes while studying or at group discussions — pencils, pen, etc.

In Section 4, a book is recommended as part of your study assignment. You may want to purchase your own copy or share with others in your group. The book is *A New Way of Living* by Michael Harper. This is the story of a church which has and is experiencing renewal.

New Life in Christ

SECTION 1

New People

SECTION 1 WEEK 1

POINT OF STUDY: As you open your life to God some definite changes begin to take place.

Study to be completed:

1 What God thinks of you

READ Psalm 139 1-18. In the space below WRITE OUT in full verse 17.

God is always with me
wherever I go

What are your thoughts about God? Have you ever prayed a prayer like the one in verses 23 and 24 of Psalm 139? READ these verses now. THINK about them.

2 What kind of relationship does God want to have with you?

READ John 1:12,13; 2 Corinthians 6:18; James 2:23; John 15:13,14; John 17:3. What do these verses tell you? WRITE your answers below.

What else has God promised? READ 2 Peter 1:3,4 in a modern translation or paraphrase. What does this verse tell you? WRITE THE ANSWER *in your own words* — don't copy the verse this time.

3

2 Peter 1:4 talks about God's promise 'to give us his own character' *(The Living Bible).* How does this happen? FIND THE ANSWER in the following verses and then WRITE it in the space beneath.
John 1:12,13; Revelation 3:20; John 14:23; 2 Corinthians 5:17.

Really believing on God makes us Sons of God

4

LOOK AGAIN at 2 Corinthians 5:17.
Has this change taken place in your life?
ANSWER: Yes
No
Dont' know
If your answer is 'No' or 'Don't know', what do you think you have to do to become 'a new creation' or, as *The Living Bible* puts it, 'a new person'?
THINK ABOUT THIS.
NOW READ pages 30 - 32 , *Believe and Receive.*

READ John 14:15-23. What do you think it means to have God the Father, Son and Holy Spirit come and make their home in your life? WRITE your answer below.

* ◯ denotes in depth assignment.

New Understanding

SECTION 1 WEEK 2

POINT OF STUDY: To grow in the Christian life you need to be getting to know God better and to be appreciating what friendship with him can mean to you.

Study to be completed:

1 What is God like?

Have you ever had to answer the question, 'What is God like?' THINK about it now. WRITE DOWN all the thoughts that come into your mind. (If you find this question difficult to answer, get together with another member of your group and think about the question together before answering it yourself. You can do this at any time during the course, if this is helpful.)

2 God as the great creator

LOOK AT the following passages. What do they tell you about God? Using the space allowed, say in as few words as possible (i.e., SUMMARISE) what each passage tells you.

Isaiah 40:28-31

Psalm 19

Psalm 147

3 God as your close friend

LOOK AT the following verses. SUMMARISE what each verse tells you about God's friendship with man.
Exodus 33:11a
(Note: Where a reference is given as 33:11a, it shows that the first part of the verse only is to be read.)

Numbers 12:7, 8a

John 15:15

4

a. THINK about God as the great Creator. What difference does it make to you to believe in God as Creator? WRITE down your answer.

b.What does friendship with God mean to you?

Character study

One method of personal bible study is to make a study of one person, e.g., the apostle Paul. The following study is about Paul. You will be thinking more about Paul as this course progresses and so will be able to add to your character study of him.
(Wrong ideas about God can cause a lot of damage. Paul started out with some very wrong ideas about God. What were they? How did he come to think differently? How did his life change as a result? Think about these questions as you complete the study below.

STUDY:

The passages given below cover some of the early incidents of Paul's life. The Ephesians' passage tells of the task God entrusted to him. WRITE in your own words the story of Paul's life as covered by these passages. Don't make it too detailed.

Acts 7:58-8:3; 9:1-30; 11:19-30; 12:25-13:3; Ephesians 3:7-10.

New Calling

SECTION 1 WEEK 3

POINT OF STUDY: You are called to live a particular kind of life: the kind of life Jesus himself lived.

Study to be completed:

1 Discover what your calling is

LOOK at Hebrews 3:1; Ephesians 1:18; 2 Timothy 1:9; 2 Thessalonians 1:11.
What do you think these verses mean when they speak about 'your calling?'
Think about this.
READ the verses in their context. COMPARE different translations or paraphrases. What do you learn about your calling as a Christian? WRITE OUT your answer.

LOOK AT 1 Peter 2:9. Note that God calls us not just as individuals, but as a people.

2

READ 1 Thessalonians 5:24.
What does God promise?

3 Spiritual growth

The fact that you have a new nature does not mean you can lie down and not bother to do anything to help yourself grow in the Christian life. Or does it? 
FIND THE ANSWER in 2 Peter 1:1-11.
READ this passage through in as many versions of the bible as you have.
What do you have to do to grow?

4 Personal application

It is essential to your spiritual growth and to your growing understanding of the bible that you continually apply its truths to your life. What area of your life is God challenging you about at the moment?

THINK ABOUT THIS AND THEN WRITE OUT YOUR ANSWER.

5 Topical study

This is another method of personal bible study. In a topical study you take a word or topic and make a study of it with the help of a bible concordance. In this study the word 'follow' is taken.

Aim of study: To help you understand what it means to follow God.

LOOK UP each verse. READ the surrounding verses and note what they say. Then RE-WRITE the verse in your own words, i.e., paraphrase it. Paraphrasing a verse or passage highlights your understanding of it.

Ephesians 5:1

1 Corinthians 14:1

Romans 14:19

1 Thessalonians 5:15

1 Timothy 6:11

Hebrews 12:14

New Relationships

SECTION 1 WEEK 4

POINT OF STUDY: God calls you to love him and to love others as you love yourself.

Study to be completed:

1

In bringing us into a loving relationship with himself God had another end in view also.
What was it?
LOOK AT 1 John 4:19-21.
WRITE OUT your answer.

See also 1 Peter 1:22

2

a. Why is it so important that we should learn to forgive quickly? LOOK AT Matthew 6:14,15; 18:21-35; Mark 11:25.
WRITE OUT your answer.

b. LIST some of the usual excuses people give for holding on to grievances.

3

a. We shall sometimes fail to do what is required of us. What provision has God made for our failing? LOOK AT 1 John 1:5-10.

b. READ 1 Timothy 1:12-17.
Paul could have had a lot on his conscience and been an extremely troubled man because of it, if he had not come to know God's forgiveness in a very real way. As well as learning how to forgive others we have to learn how to receive forgiveness ourselves. THINK ABOUT THIS.

4

Jesus nevertheless expects a lot of those who follow him. READ Matthew Chapter 5 in a modern translation or paraphrase.

Does God ever ask of you something which is impossible?

THINK ABOUT THIS.

LOOK AGAIN at Week 3, New Calling, 2.

LOOK AT John 13:34, 35; Romans 12:9,10; Hebrews 13:1.

ANSWER THE FOLLOWING QUESTIONS:

a. What was new about the commandment that Jesus gave to the twelve disciples (John 13:34,35)?

b. How can we express our love so that others can really feel it and benefit from it? THINK ABOUT THIS. WRITE OUT YOUR ANSWER.

Addendum

Believe and receive

Do you want to become a Christian?

Do you believe that:

(a) Jesus Christ is the Son of God?

'Anyone who believes and says that Jesus is the Son of God has God living in him, and he is living with God' (1 John 4:15).

(b) God loves you and sent his Son to die on the Cross for you and for all mankind?

'God showed how much he loved us by sending his only Son into this wicked world to bring to us eternal life through his death. In this act we see what real love is: it is not our love for God, but his love for us when he sent his Son to satisfy God's anger against our sins' (1 John 4:9,10).

(c) Jesus Christ rose from the dead and is living now, that he wants to help you, to hear and answer your prayers?

'...he is the one who died for us and came back to life again for us and is sitting at the place of highest honour next to God, pleading for us there in heaven' (Romans 8:34).

If your answer is yes to the above questions, have you accepted Jesus Christ as your Saviour and made him your Lord? Have you received the gift of the Holy Spirit?

'Each one of you must turn from sin, return to God and be baptized in the name of Jesus Christ for the forgiveness of your sins; then you also shall receive this gift, the Holy Spirit' (Acts 2:38).

If you want to become a Christian you must be willing to turn from those things which have separated you from God. Jesus Christ died so that you could live an entirely new life.

'He personally carried the load of our sins in his own body when he died on the cross, so that we can be finished with sin and live a good life from now on.' (1 Peter 2:24).

Are you prepared for this kind of change to take place in your life? If so, then you are ready to take the step of becoming a Christian.

Believe on Jesus

'Believe on the Lord Jesus and you will be saved...' (Acts 16:31).

'...to all who received him, he gave the right to become children of God. All they needed to do was to trust him to save them' (John 1:12).

To believe on is to put your trust in, to commit yourself to, to rely upon.

If this is what you want to do — to put your trust in, to commit yourself to, to rely upon Jesus Christ — then talk to God about it, using words like the following:

Dear Father
I believe that you love me and that you sent your Son to die on the Cross for me. I believe that he rose triumphant over sin and death and that through him I can come to you and receive the gift of eternal life. I confess my sin and ask forgiveness for all the wrong I have done.

I turn from sin and wrongdoing and as from this moment I am trusting in Jesus Christ to save and help me.

As you take this step a change takes place.
'...all those who believe this are reborn — not a physical rebirth resulting from human passion or plan, but from the will of God' (John 1:13).

Make him your Lord

Jesus said that following him would mean saying 'No' to oneself. To be a slave to one's own selfish desires leads only to unhappiness. Peace and joy come through letting Christ rule in one's life.

As you read your bible you will discover the rules or commandments God has given, but there is one rule which sums up all the others and that is the rule of love (Galatians 5:14; Matthew 22:37-40).

How do you get on with other people? Do you hold a resentment or a grudge against anyone? Is there someone you should forgive? Jesus taught us to pray '...forgive us our sins just as we have forgiven those who have sinned against us' (Matthew 6:12). Now is the time to think over your relationships with others, particularly with those closest to you, those with whom you live and work. It is up to you to put your part right and to begin to learn to love others as Jesus loves them.

There will be times when you will fail, for it is impossible for us to keep God's law and never to fail. That is why Jesus had to die for us. But we don't have to try to keep God's commandments through our own strength or will power. The Holy Spirit who comes to live within us makes us different people, and he will produce this kind of fruit in us: love, joy, peace, patience, kindness, goodness, faithfulness, gentleness and self-control (Galatians 5:22,23).

Receive the Holy Spirit

John the Baptist pointed to Jesus as '...the Lamb of God who takes away the world's sin' and as '...the one who baptizes with (or in) the Holy Spirit' (John 1:29,33).

The Holy Spirit is a person, the third person of the Trinity. He makes us witnesses to Jesus. As you read your bible find out all you can about the Holy Spirit. When the first Christians received the Spirit on the day of Pentecost they knew something tremendous had happened to them. Read the account in Acts 2. God wants to do the same for you. Ask him to baptize you in the Holy Spirit. This can happen in the privacy of your own home or through the laying of hands. Read Acts 8:7; 9:17; 19:6.

Pray, read your bible, join a Church

Set aside a certain time each day to pray and read the bible. Begin by reading one of the gospels and then read through the Acts of the Apostles. Read prayerfully. It is a good idea to put a little mark against those passages that you don't understand and later ask your minister or a responsible Christian whom you can trust to explain them to you. Remember the important thing is to put into practice the things you do understand. This is the way to grow in the Christian life.

Join a church if you are not already a member of one. You need the help, advice and encouragement of other Christians. And they need you too. If possible become part of a group that meets regularly for prayer and bible study.

Live as a son of God

In all that you do, remember that God is with you, and that you now have a special relationship with him. You have acknowledged him as your Father, accepted his gift of eternal life; you are his son, he calls you his dearly beloved child (Romans 8:14-17).

Unless otherwise stated, quotations are from *The Living Bible.*

BELIEVE AND RECEIVE is available as a leaflet from Celebration Publishing. Other similar teaching leaflets are also available.

The Holy Spirit

SECTION 2

Introduction

As an introduction to this section answer the following questions. Don't refer to your bible or to any books or notes. WRITE DOWN whatever thoughts come into your mind.

1

Who is the Holy Spirit?

2

What particular tasks have been assigned to him?

3

How does the Holy Spirit help you in your life? Have there been particular times when you have been aware of his helping you? GIVE DETAILS.

New Power

SECTION 2 WEEK 1

POINT OF STUDY: The Holy Spirit is sent to help you. He comes to live within you — indwelling your innermost being and personality. His life is continually available to fill and empower you.

Study to be completed:

1 What Jesus had to say about the Holy Spirit

Jesus had a lot to say to his friends about the person and work of the Holy Spirit. READ the conversation in John Chapters 14, 15 and 16.

Having read these chapters, go back and LOOK AGAIN at 14:16,17,26; 15:26; 16:7-15. Jesus was very specific about the role the Holy Spirit was to play in the lives of these men. What does it mean to have one indwelling us who is such a Counsellor or Comforter and also the Spirit of Truth?

WRITE DOWN your thoughts about this.

2

There was something more that Jesus had to say later on about the Holy Spirit. READ Acts 1:1-11. ANSWER the questions below:

a. What phrase did Jesus use to describe the event that was to happen 'before many days' (v.5)?

b. What were the disciples going to receive (v.8)?

3

Jesus himself was empowered for service

READ Luke 3:21,22; 4:14-19.

He empowers others. He is the baptizer in the Holy Spirit.

READ Matthew 3:11; Mark 1:8; Luke 3:16; John 1:33,34.

4

READ Acts 2:1-21.

Try to picture this event in your mind. What do you think it felt like?

In your own words DESCRIBE the reactions of the crowd that gathered (verses 5-13).

Peter told the people that they were witnessing the fulfilment of a prophecy given by an Old Testament prophet some 400 years before. See if you can find the place in the Old Testament where this prophecy was given. If you have a bible with a reference margin, this will help you. Turn to the prophecy and read it.

The following questions are difficult ones, as probably there are no neat, tidy answers to them. Don't worry if you feel you don't know the right answers — opinions differ anyway. What do you think?

a. LOOK AGAIN at John 14-17. What do you think Jesus meant when he said 'for he (the Holy Spirit) dwells with you, and will be in you?'

b. LOOK AGAIN at Acts 1:8. Here Jesus talks about the Holy Spirit coming upon them. Was this to be a further experience?

c. READ John 20:19-23. THINK ABOUT this passage in relation to the events that took place on the day of Pentecost (Acts 2:1-21). When do you think the disciples 'received the Spirit?' If they 'received the Spirit' before Pentecost, what did they receive on the day of Pentecost?

This whole study on the Holy Spirit is an important one because today Christians all over the world are experiencing the power of the Holy Spirit in ways very similar to those recorded in the Acts of the Apostles. It would probably help you to do some reading on this subject in order to discover what is happening and what people think about it. Some leaflets and books will be recommended to you at your next group meeting.

New Gifts

SECTION 2 WEEK 2

POINT OF STUDY: The effect the Holy Spirit can make upon a group of people who are open to receive his gifts and power.

Study to be completed:

1

Over the next two or three days READ the ACTS OF THE APOSTLES in a modern paraphrase such as *The Living Bible* or J. B. Phillips' translation. If possible, put an evening or some hours in the day aside to sit down and read the book straight through at one sitting. Reading through a book of the bible like this without stopping can be an exciting experience. If you cannot find such an uninterrupted period read it through in odd moments as possible. If you cannot manage to read the whole book over the next few days read up to the end of Chapter 12 before going on to complete this study.

2

Having completed your reading of the Acts of the Apostles READ AND CONSIDER the following passage taken from J. B. Phillips' preface to his translation:

It is impossible to spend several months in the close study of this remarkable short book, conventionally known as the Acts of the Apostles, without being profoundly stirred and, to be honest, disturbed. The reader is stirred because he is seeing Christianity, the real thing, in action for the first time in human history. The new-born Church, as vulnerable as any human child, having neither money nor influence nor power in the ordinary sense, is setting forth joyfully and courageously to win the pagan world for God, through Christ. The young Church, like all young creatures, is appealing in its simplicity and single-heartedness. Here we are seeing the Church in its first youth — valiant and unspoiled — a body of ordinary men and women joined in an unconquerable fellowship never before seen on this earth.

Yet we cannot help feeling disturbed as well as moved, for this surely is the Church as it was meant to be. It is vigorous and flexible, for these are days before it ever became fat and short of breath through prosperity, or muscle-bound by over-organisation. These men did not make 'acts of faith', they believed; they did not 'say their prayers', they really prayed. They did not hold conferences on psychosomatic medicine, they simply healed the sick. But if they were uncomplicated and naive by modern standards we have ruefully to admit that they were open on the God-ward side in a way that is almost unknown today.

No one can read this book without being convinced that there is Someone here at work besides mere human beings. Perhaps because of their very simplicity, perhaps because of their readiness to believe, to obey, to give, to suffer, and if need be to die, the Spirit of God found what surely He must always be seeking — a fellowship of men and women so united in love and faith that He can work in them and through them with a minimum of let or hindrance. Consequently it is a matter of sober historical fact that never before has any small body of ordinary people so moved the world that their enemies could say, with tears of rage in their eyes, that these men 'have turned the world upside down'!

3

a. LOOK AGAIN at the last paragraph of the above quotation. What impression did J. B. Phillips gain of the early Christians as he worked on his translation of Acts? LIST below the things he mentions.

b. Why do you think these early Christians were so strong and made such an impact on those around them?

c. What qualities does the church need to be effective nowadays? In general, how does it compare with the early church?

4

a. In your reading of Acts, what was your impression of the part played by miraculous or supernatural happenings? NOTE below two or three incidents that stood out to you.

b. If this element had been absent, do you think the young church would have grown so fast?

READ 1 Corinthians 12:4-11. This is a list of the gifts or manifestations of the Holy Spirit. In reading through Acts you will have noticed many of these gifts in operation. There is a school of thought among some theologians that these supernatural gifts or manifestations of the Spirit were only given for the early period of the church's history in order to bring the church into being and they were never intended to be permanent.

What do you think? WRITE your answer below.

New Battles

SECTION 2 WEEK 3

POINT OF STUDY: The deeper your spiritual experience the more battles you will encounter. God allows this to happen to change and strengthen you.

Study to be completed:

1

READ Luke 4:1-15.
What happened to Jesus after the Holy Spirit had come upon him at his baptism? In your own words DESCRIBE the ways in which Satan tempted him.

The more you experience the work of the Holy Spirit in your life the more Satan will seek to undo that work. God allows this to happen for he can turn it to good. As you are tested and tried so you are being strengthened and changed.

We have a perfect pattern to follow in the life and death and teaching of Jesus Christ. God wants to change us into the likeness of Jesus Christ. SEE 2 Corinthians 3:18. Change is a painful process and you will have many ups and downs in your life as God allows you to go through many difficult experiences in order to bring about this change.

In Matthew 3:11 it says of Jesus that 'he will baptize you with the Holy Spirit and   ' (FILL IN WORD). Fire burns up the dross — the impurities in your life. As you experience more of the Holy Spirit you need to expect the 'and fire'.

2

The following verses or passages all illustrate the way Satan works in people's lives — sometimes without their even being aware of it. Briefly SUMMARISE against each of the following verses or passages how Satan was at work.

1 Chronicles 21:1, 7

SAMPLE ANSWER: Satan tempted David to do something displeasing to God.

Job 1; 2:1-7

Matthew 16:21-23

John 8 (note particularly v. 44)

Luke 22:31-34

John 13:2

Acts 5:3

2 Corinthians 12:7

3

a. There are certain precautions we need to take in learning how to deal with Satan. What advice is given in the following passages?

Ephesians 4:26-27

2 Corinthians 2:10-11

James 4:6-10

1 Peter 5:5-11

b. RE-WRITE in your own words (paraphrase) the following verse:

1 Corinthians 10:13

4

As this study has shown, we have an enemy — the devil — who is out to trip us up and make things difficult for us. We also have ourselves to contend with — the weakness of our own flesh; and the world can offer us many counter attractions to God's way. SEE such verses as Gal. 5:17; James 1:14 and 1 John 2:14-17.

In Hebrews 4:15 we read that 'we have not a high priest who is unable to sympathise with our weaknesses, but one who in every respect has been tempted as we are, yet without sinning. Let us then with confidence draw near to the throne of grace, that we may receive mercy and find grace to help in time of need'.

Jesus went through many experiences for our sake in order to identify with us in our weakness. He understands the difficulties and the temptations we face and can help us in just the right way at the right time.

(5) God's armour

READ Ephesians 6:10-17.
From this passage what do you understand you need to do to 'be able to stand against all the wiles of the devil?'

This passage is a difficult one to understand and apply to oneself. WRITE DOWN what thoughts you have and then, if possible, turn to a commentary or commentaries and see what help they give you.

YOUR THOUGHTS ON THE PASSAGE

WHAT THE COMMENTARIES SAY

New Walk

SECTION 2 WEEK 4

POINT OF STUDY: To be filled with the Spirit you need to open your life continuously to his power and direction.

Study to be completed:

1 Following the Holy Spirit's directions

LOOK at Ephesians 5:18-20 and Galatians 5:16-26. READ the Galatians passage in a modern translation or paraphrase, preferably *The Living Bible.* Galatians 5:25 in *The Living Bible* well sums up the point of this study. To impress this verse on your mind, COPY IT below:

2 Things to avoid

The Holy Spirit is a person. All you do and think affects him. Remember he lives in you and when you grieve or hurt him you will feel inner conflict. This may take the form of such feelings as frustration, anger, depression etc. From the following passages, LIST ways in which you can grieve or hurt the Holy Spirit.

Ephesians 4:30-32; 1 Thessalonians 4:1-8; 5:19-22; Galatians 5:16-21,26.

3 Things to do

PARAPHRASE (re-write in your own words) Colossians 3:12-17.

4

A lack of trust in God can hinder our following 'the Holy Spirit's leading in every part of our lives'. It was this that hindered the Israelites from entering into all that God had for them.

READ Hebrews 3:7-19; 4:1,2.

What things encourage you to trust God?

5 The Holy Spirit's sword

Ephesians 6:17b says that the sword of the Spirit is the word of God. In what ways is it a sword? How are you to make use of it? With the aid of a concordance find scriptures to help you answer these two questions.

Gifts of the Holy Spirit

SECTION 3

New Communication

SECTION 3 WEEK 1

POINT OF STUDY: God gives gifts to his people for them to use for their own spiritual growth and for the building up of the body of Christ. In this section you will be discovering some of the gifts which God has given and how he wants you to use them. This study considers, in particular, speaking in tongues, interpretation and prophecy.

For those of you who have not experienced the operation of these gifts, this section may seem rather theoretical. Paul's advice to the Corinthian church was to 'make love your aim, and earnestly desire the spiritual gifts' (1 Corinthians 14:1) As you study, let this be your aim and desire too.

Study to be completed:

1

READ 1 Corinthians Chapters 12, 13 and 14. Read them carefully and thoughtfully. Note down any verses or passages you find hard to understand.

2

a. LOOK AGAIN at 1 Corinthians 12:8-11. Make a LIST of the various gifts mentioned.

b. LOOK AGAIN at 1 Corinthians 12:4-7; 14:12. SEE ALSO Ephesians 4:11,12. Of what use are these gifts? How are they to be used?

3 Speaking in tongues

a. LOOK AGAIN at 2 Corinthians 14:1-5. ANSWER the following questions: What are you told to do (verses 1,5)?

When you speak in a tongue who are you speaking to (verse 2)?

If you prophesy who is helped (verses 3,4)?

If you speak in a tongue who is helped (verse 4)?

Where does the gift of interpretation fit in (verse 5)?
Note also 1 Corinthians 14:13.

b. In 1 Corinthians 14 is Paul encouraging or discouraging speaking in tongues? What do you think? WRITE OUT your answer.

4 Prophecy

In Joel 2:28, Joel prophesied that when the Spirit would be poured out then 'your sons and daughters shall prophesy'. On the day of Pentecost Peter recognised that this was what was happening (Acts 2:14-21).

READ Acts 2:5-11; 10:46; 11:27-30; 13:1-3 and NOTE how prophecy was used to build up the church.

Prophecy is 'for upbuilding, encouragement and consolation' (1 Corinthians 14:3). However, 1 Thessalonians 5:19-21 and 1 Corinthians 14:29-32 both speak of the need to judge prophecy. How does one judge prophecy? WRITE DOWN your thoughts about this. Can you find examples in scripture of prophecy being judged? NOTE DOWN any you can find.

New Revelation

SECTION 3 WEEK 2

POINT OF STUDY: This study looks at three more of the gifts or manifestations of the Holy Spirit — the word of wisdom, the word of knowledge and the discerning of spirits. It underlines the fact that these gifts are not to be sought or used casually.

Study to be completed:

1

a. READ Isaiah 11:2. What does this passage tell you about the Holy Spirit?

Isaiah 11:1-5 speaks of the Spirit resting upon Jesus. SEE Isaiah 61:1,2a; Luke 4:18,19.

b. All wisdom and knowledge come from God. He is able to discern right from wrong and to judge fairly. From his store of wisdom and knowledge he is able to give specific information or direction in a given situation. LOOK AT 1 Corinthians 12:8-10 (Authorised Version). Here are three gifts of the Spirit described as
the . . . . of wisdom
the. . . . . of knowledge
. . . . of spirits

FILL IN GAPS.

2 Word of wisdom

a. READ Luke 2:40-52; Matthew 13:53-58; 22:15-22. NOTE that Jesus was 'filled with wisdom', that he 'increased in wisdom' and that there were times when he spoke a particular 'word of wisdom'.

b. LOOK AT Matthew 21:23-27; Acts 6:9-10; 15:13-21. These are examples of the word of wisdom in operation.

c. The word of wisdom is a gift of the Spirit given at a specific moment in time for a particular situation. It is important, however, not just to seek the gift but to seek to increase in wisdom as Jesus did.

LOOK AT Proverbs 2:1-6. How can you increase in wisdom? THINK ABOUT THIS.

3 Word of knowledge

a. LOOK AT Luke 6:6-11; John 1:43-51; 4:1-26; Acts 5:1-11; 9:10-19. These are examples of the word of knowledge in operation.

b. LOOK AGAIN at the above passages, completing the study below. NOTE in each case how the people concerned reacted. Against each incident SUMMARISE how they reacted. At end, ANSWER the question: What do you learn from this?

Luke 6:6-11

SAMPLE ANSWER: The Pharisees were furious that Jesus knew their thoughts and that he acted as he did. As a result they plotted evil against him.

John 1:43-51

John 4:1-26

Acts 5:1-11

Acts 9:10-19

WHAT DO YOU LEARN FROM THIS?

4 Discerning of spirits

a. READ Mark 5:1-13; Luke 4:33-37. NOTE the authority which Jesus had over the spirits.

b. READ Luke 9:1; 10:1,2,17-20.
Why were the 'seventy' so delighted (Luke 10:17)?

What did Jesus say to them in reply?

Why do you think he made a point of saying this?

WRITE DOWN YOUR THOUGHTS.

c. NOTE these other incidents of the discerning of spirits: Luke 13:10-13; Matthew 16:21-23; Luke 9:52-56 (read in Authorised Version if possible); Acts 16:16-18; Acts 8:9-24.

a. LOOK AGAIN at Acts 16:16-18. Why do you think Paul was annoyed and finally rebuked the spirit, even though the slave girl was 'speaking the truth'?

b. LOOK AGAIN at Acts 8:9-24. Why do you think Peter rebuked Simon? What was wrong?

New Works

SECTION 3 WEEK 3

POINT OF STUDY: This study looks at the three most spectacular gifts of the Spirit listed in 1 Corinthians 12 – the gift of faith, the working of miracles and gifts of healing. Today Jesus works through his body on earth – we too, therefore, can expect the miraculous element to be present.

Study to be completed:

1

In the gifts of the Spirit it is not always possible to tell exactly which gift is in operation at any one time; often several gifts are being manifested at the same time. This is particularly true in the case of these three gifts – the gift of faith, the working of miracles and gifts of healing.

The gift of faith is 'special faith' given for a particular situation. By it the recipient is enabled to trust God for the miraculous. Some healings and all miracles call for a 'special faith'. The miraculous element is more present in some healings than in others; not all miracles, however, are miracles of healings. NOTE the various elements present in the following incidents:
John 2:1-11; 5:2-9; 6:1-14; 11:1-47.
Acts 3:1-10; 9:36-42; 28:1-6.

2

a. Was Jesus ever limited in what he was able to do? LOOK AT Matthew 13:53-58. COMPARE Matthew 9:22; Mark 5:34; 10:52; Luke 17:19.

b. Jesus often rebuked the disciples for their lack of faith. SEE Matthew 6:30; 8:26; 14:31; 17:14-20. From these passages NOTE DOWN the different things for which he expected them to have faith.

c. Sometimes the disciples had tremendous faith; at other times they seemed totally lacking in it. Later on in the Acts of the Apostles we see them moving and acting with a far greater assurance of faith.

How do you think faith grows? FIND scriptures which help you to answer this question.

WRITE DOWN your answer.

3

Paul talks about 'faith working through love' (Galatians 5:6) and of love as 'the more excellent way' to the working of the gifts of the Spirit (1 Corinthians 12:31). What moved Jesus to heal the sick and to work miracles?

LOOK AT Matthew 14:14; 15:32.

Often in the gospels we read that Jesus had compassion on people or on a person. With the aid of your concordance find other places in the bible where this word is used. NOTE DOWN the verses or passages and what they say.

What do you think the word 'compassion' means?
WRITE OUT what you think it means.

Now LOOK UP the word in a dictionary. COMPARE your answer.

Have you ever felt a tremendous compassion for a person or persons?
THINK ABOUT THIS.

4

In the life and ministry of Jesus we see a perfect life, a total giving of himself to others. He had that perfect assurance that whatever he asked of his Father it would be done. SEE John 11:41,42. There were no unanswered prayers as far as Jesus was concerned. Do the following scriptures give you some clue as to why this was so? READ these scriptures through in several different versions.
John 4:34; 5:19,30
Philippians 2:5-11
Matthew 20:25-28

What do these passages tell you about Jesus? What kind of person was he? How did he think? How did he act?

GIVE YOUR ANSWERS BELOW.

Review what you have learnt so far from Section 3. What relevance have these things to the church today? Think about the church you belong to. What things have struck you as relevant — or irrelevant?

WRITE YOUR THOUGHTS below.

New Love

SECTION 3 WEEK 4

POINT OF STUDY: In seeking to discover more about the gifts of the Spirit you need to be seeking to love more deeply. As you feel God's love for people he will be able to trust you with gifts for them.

Study to be completed:

Complete chapter analysis of 1 Corinthians 13 as follows:

1

Read the chapter through carefully once or twice and then summarise it in your own words. Your summary should be brief, but should cover all the key thoughts of the chapter.

SUMMARY

2

From your summary pick out the key thoughts and find two or three cross references for each of them.

KEY THOUGHTS	CROSS REFERENCES

3

Are there parts of this chapter that you find it hard to understand? If so, note down what the difficulty is.

DIFFICULTIES WITH TEXT:

4

a. What has impressed you in studying this chapter? What has the Holy Spirit been saying to you? Write out a personal application.

PERSONAL APPLICATION

Once you have analysed a chapter like this keep it for future reference and be open to learn all you can from other people, from books and commentaries and make notes of anything that is helpful — adding them to your study. In particular, see what help you can find in answering any difficulties you have noted down. You can use this method for studying other chapters of the bible.

b. Why do you think Paul laid such emphasis on the importance of love in relation to the gifts of the Spirit?

(5) Ministries in the body of Christ

a. READ Romans 12:4-8; 1 Corinthians 12:1-11, 27-30; Ephesians 4:4-14. You will notice that in these passages gifts are mentioned such a prophecy, gifts of healing, etc.; at other times a function or ministry, such as prophets, healers, etc. The latter are ministries which God has given to people. Pick out the different ministries mentioned and make a list of them below.

b. ANSWER the following questions. Can you find scriptures that help you to answer them? If so, note them down. If not, just give your own answers.

What purpose do these ministries fulfil in a church?

What are the necessary qualities for persons fulfilling such ministries?

How can such ministries be encouraged?

Addendum

We have now introduced you to several different ways of studying the bible. More will be said about this in Section 4, Week 2, How to study together. In these next sections there are fewer study questions, the emphasis being more on group sharing and on encouraging you to widen your knowledge by reading and listening to tapes.

An Introduction to Sections 4,5 and 6

Section 4

In this section we encourage you to write down thoughts that come to you each week as you pray and read the bible. This is as an aid to sharing your thoughts with others. Maybe you don't have set times when you read the bible or pray. People differ in the pattern they find most helpful. However, your sharing may help someone else who wants to learn more about personal prayer and bible reading.

Also we suggest you read a book as part of your study assignment for this section. The book is *A New Way of Living* by Michael Harper, a paperback published by Hodder and Stoughton. This is the story of a church which has and is experiencing renewal. This book can be obtained from Christian bookshops.

Section 5

Four short recorded talks will be played at your weekly meetings. Space is provided each week for you to make notes as you listen to these talks.

Section 6

In this final section we ask you to review the earlier sections and to evaluate what you have learnt from the course. Space is given for you to summarise your thoughts and feelings.

Serving Together

SECTION 4

How To Pray Together

SECTION 4 WEEK 1

POINT OF STUDY: When you meet together to pray all should come ready to contribute to the meeting; preparation beforehand is important.

Study to be completed:

'When you come together, each one has...' (1 Corinthians 14:26). It seems Paul took it for granted that when a group of Christians came together everyone would have something to contribute. Life begins to flow in a group when each person comes to give as well as to receive. In order to be able to do this you need to be praying and reading your bible at home; to take time to listen to God and to think about what you hear him saying to you. In particular, you need to take time to do this before you come to the prayer meeting.

'Preparation begins at home... The prayer meeting is not the time to catch up spiritually! The person who comes totally unprepared is likely to be a dead weight in the group and to go away feeling worse rather than better as a result! Such preparation involves not only the reading, but the doing of God's word.' (Quotation taken from *When You Come Together,* Post Green Teaching Booklet).

ANSWER the following questions:

Do you have a regular time of prayer and bible reading?

What system (if any) of bible reading do you follow?

How do you hear God speak to you? List ways in which he speaks to you.

As you learn to listen to God he will speak to you about your own personal life, about those for whom you are praying and also about the church or fellowship to which you belong. You need to share these thoughts with others, as this will help you to decide whether it really is God speaking. Sometimes it is possible to get muddled about what we think God is saying.

Prayer is not just asking, prayer is contact. Jesus said of himself, 'Truly, truly, I say to you, the Son can do nothing of his own accord, but only what he sees the Father doing; for whatever he does, that the Son does likewise' (John 5:19). Jesus kept very close to his Father; the life that he lived and the works that he did flowed out of this relationship. Jesus saw people and situations through the eyes of his Father in heaven and acted accordingly. We too need to see people and situations through God's eyes and to act as he directs us. Our willingness to be involved in the answers to our own prayers may well show how earnest our prayers are and how much we really care. Prayer is involvement.

Nothing kills one's own prayer life or the church prayer meeting so much as praying for the same things week after week and never seeing anything happen. There is always the need to stop and ask, 'What is God saying about this?', 'What does he want us to do about it?'

In this way the Holy Spirit can give to a group of people an understanding of what he wants that church or fellowship to become. A number of bible passages talk about the need for us to have a 'vision' of what God can or wants to do in a situation. See 1 Samuel 3:1; Habakkuk 2:2,3; Acts 26:15-19. One dictionary definition of the word vision is 'imaginative insight, statesmanlike foresight, political sagacity'. Such vision is important. 'Where there is no vision the people perish' (Proverbs 29:18).

Over the next four weeks we suggest you make a point of noting down thoughts which come to you in your times of personal prayer and bible reading. Space for this is provided at the end of each week's study section. There will be opportunity at your group meetings for you to share some of these thoughts and this will help you to get used to sharing with others the things you feel God is saying. You will find that what you have to share will often help others, and that to share your thoughts in this way will be a help to you too.

Study questions:

1

READ the following passages, NOTE their context. LIST below what these scriptures tell you to do.

Ephesians 6:18; Colossians 3:16,17; Hebrews 10:25; 1 Timothy 2:1,2; 1 Corinthians 14:26.

What strikes you most from this list? Why?

2

READ the following passages and note the way Paul prayed for others. LIST the things he asked God to do for them.

Ephesians 1:16-23; 3:14-21; Colossians 1:9-12.

How often do you pray for others? How do you pray for them? What are your expectations that God is able to do what you ask? What action are you taking to help those for whom you are praying?

THINK ABOUT THESE QUESTIONS.

3 Glimpses of the early church at prayer

STUDY the passages in their context. Against each incident ANSWER the following questions: What was the situation? How did the people concerned pray? What did God do? What do you learn (if anything) about the people involved and the way they acted?

a. Acts 4:24-31

Acts 12:5-17

Acts 13:1-3

b. Acts 20:36-38. Here is a picture of Paul praying with others. Note the context. What was the situation? What do you learn from this incident? What picture does this give you of the early church?

Remember, that part of your study assignment for this section is to read Michael Harper's *A New Way of Living.* If you have not yet obtained a copy or arranged to share one, do so this week.

SPACE IS PROVIDED BELOW FOR YOU TO WRITE DOWN THOUGHTS THAT COME TO YOU DURING THE WEEK AS YOU PRAY AND READ THE BIBLE.

How to Study Together

SECTION 4 WEEK 2

POINT OF STUDY: To help you assess the value of personal bible study and of taking time to prepare yourself for group study.

Study to be completed:

Read the following through several times. Take time to think about what you have read. Answer the questions.

How far have you progressed in your knowledge of the bible? How easily do you remember what you have learnt? If people ask you questions about the Christian faith, do you still need to pass them on for their answers to others who are more informed than you are?

Studying the bible is different from reading. What do you think the word 'study' means? WRITE DOWN what you think it means.

Now COMPARE your answers with the definition given in a dictionary. NOTE BELOW some of the things the dictionary says about the meaning of the word 'study'.

If you want to increase your knowledge of the bible then you need to put aside time for study in addition to regular prayer and bible reading. In the first part of this course we introduced you to several ways of studying the bible. There is an addendum to this section which outlines the various principles and different types of study introduced. There are other ways to study the bible. You will find plenty of books in Christian bookshops which can help you. Your minister should be able to advise you as to the best approach for you, if you want to pursue this further.

Consider how much time you should be giving to bible study. Be realistic about the time you can give to it. It is better to decide on less time and keep to it than aim too high and never keep to it. An hour or two a week is probably a good average. Some may prefer to spend more time than this, some less.

ANSWER the following questions:

Do you already have a time when you study the bible in addition to your regular time of prayer and bible reading?

What system of study, if any, are you following? Write NONE if this is your answer.

What books of the bible would you most like to study?

What bible characters interest you most?

The bible has something to say about all the important issues of life. Have you ever thought 'I'd like to know what the bible has to say about...?' List topics you would like to study.

Your answers to the above questions could well be where your programme of personal bible study should start, though you may want to wait until you have completed your *Expressing His Life* studies. Remember don't try to do too much all at once.

To be part of a bible study group is an aid to personal study. A study group need not meet weekly; sometimes fortnightly or monthly is better as this gives more time for preparation.

A lending library with a pool of bibles, concordances, commentaries and other aids is very helpful, particularly if they can be kept in a place where people can come and actually spend time studying. Sometimes it is difficult to find anywhere quiet at home.

By the way, have you started reading *A New Way of Living yet?*

Study questions:

1

READ 2 Timothy 2:15. Why was Paul's advice to Timothy so important? If you have time read quickly through 2 Timothy, preferably in a modern version such as *The Living Bible.* A reading of this book will help you in answering the above question. WRITE your answer below.

Do you think every Christian needs to take Paul's advice to Timothy to heart? If so, why?

2

READ Acts 17:1-12, note particularly verse 11. This verse mentions not only what our attitude should be to new learning and experiences, but also one way of searching out the truth for ourselves. What other ways are there? COMMENT on this.

READ Hebrews 5:11-14; 6:1,2,9-12. COMPARE 1 Peter 2:2. FIND OUT what you can about the Epistle to the Hebrews. ANSWER the following questions: To whom was it written? Why did they need to be given such severe warnings? What message is there here for Christians today?

Have you started to read *A New Way of Living* yet?

SPACE IS PROVIDED BELOW FOR YOU TO WRITE DOWN THOUGHTS THAT COME TO YOU DURING THE WEEK AS YOU PRAY AND READ THE BIBLE.

Addendum

Different ways of studying the Bible

We have introduced you to several different ways of studying the bible. For instance:

Use of set questions

We directed your attention to various bible verses or passages and set you specific questions to think about and answer. In reading or studying the bible, there are certain basic questions you can ask yourself which will help you to think through on what you are reading — such questions as, 'What does this passage teach me about God?', 'What does it teach me about living the Christian life?', 'What is God saying to me through this passage?'. Writing your thoughts down helps you to be specific in answering such questions.

Character Study

On page 18 we introduced you to certain aspects of Paul's life and ministry. Character studies are fun to do and in doing them you can learn a lot about yourself as well as about the individual you are studying. In studying a character you should seek to discover something of the person's **background,** his **calling,** his **weaknesses,** his **strengths, what he accomplished** and **how he accomplished it.** Try sometime doing a character study of Paul. You have already learnt quite a lot about him in these studies. Later go back over what you have learnt and then add to it using the suggestions given above.

Topical study

Topical because a 'topic' or 'subject' is taken and explored to help you discover what the bible has to say on that particular subject. On page 23 we introduced you to this method of study.

Analysis study

In Section 3 you completed a chapter analysis of 1 Corinthians 13. Analysis means to take a verse, passage or chapter apart, bit by bit; to examine it in detail and to see it in relation to other similar passages elsewhere in the bible. This method can also be used to analyse a book. In analysing a book the following headings are useful:

a. By whom was it written?
b. When was it written?
c. To whom was it written?
d. Why was it written?
e. What does it say?
f. What application is there in it for me?

In your studies so far you have also discovered how to make use of cross references, the value of a bible concordance and of consulting commentaries and how to re-write a passage in your own words (paraphrase). We hope you will continue to do regular bible study and to build up your own set of notes on the bible. In doing so remember:

a. To work out a system for keeping your notes in a way that is easy and workable for you.
b. Add to them as you do further reading and study, particularly as you read relevant books and commentaries. It is important that you should add to your own study by finding out what others have to say, but don't forget you will retain more by doing some research of your own as well.
c. Personal application of what you study is essential if it is to mean anything to you and to make a difference in your life.

If *Expressing His Life* is your first introduction to studying the bible and you feel you need more encouragement before you can step out on your own then the following course may be of help to you:

THE ROAD TO EMMAUS by Daphne Mills. A question and answer bible study course in three parts. Covers basic doctrine for use by Christians young and old. Available from: Celebration Publishing.

How to Worship Together

SECTION 4 WEEK 3

POINT OF STUDY: In worship we reach out to God and at the same time are bound more closely to our brothers and sisters in Christ. It involves a very real giving of ourselves to God and to others.

Study to be completed:

Read the following through several times. Take time to think about what you have read. Answer the questions put to you at the end.

'And so, dear brothers, now we may walk right into the very Holy of Holies where God is, because of the blood of Jesus' (Hebrews 10:19, *The Living Bible*). In Old Testament times only the priests could enter the inner sanctuary of the temple, and they offered sacrifices on behalf of the people. Because of Jesus' death on the cross we can come very simply and easily into God's presence. But this does not mean we should do so without any preparation; a casual approach produces a casual knowledge of God. Before you come together with others to praise and worship God you need to make sure that you personally are in the right frame of mind and spirit, that you have confessed any known sin, and that you are in a right relationship with God and others. Only as you prepare yourself in this way will you be free to enter into praise and worship.

Your experience of worshipping together as a body of people will to a certain extent be the sum total of how closely you have individually walked with God the rest of the week.

To worship God is to enter into that place where your heart and mind are still and not full of restless activity and worry. 'Be still and know that I am God' (Psalm 46:10). You need to be constantly bringing yourself back to the place where you are at peace and at rest in yourself. In this way you will carry the sense of the presence of God with you wherever you go and will be able to come quickly into the experience of worship when you are called to do so.

It is not a matter of worshipping God when you feel like it. Worship is something God expects of one and there is at first often an effort involved in this giving of oneself. One can so easily allow one's own moods and feelings to dominate and to keep one from entering into praise.

While it is important to learn how to pray and how to share the word of God with others, the place at which you will be involved most deeply together in Christ is in worship. To experience the wonder of being bonded together into a worshipping family each member must be willing to give of himself at a very deep level to God and to all his brothers and sisters at the same time. Love has to be expressed not only to God, but also to one another.

THINK PARTICULARLY ABOUT THIS STATEMENT: 'To experience the wonder of being bonded together into a worshipping family each member must be willing to give of himself at a very deep level to God and to all his brothers and sisters at the same time.'

What do you think this means? APPLY the thought to yourself. What does it mean for you? WRITE your answers below.

Study questions

1

READ John 4:19-24. How does God want us to worship him? In your own words explain what you think verse 24 means.

2

READ Romans 12:1,2 (R.S.V.). This passage gives a wider meaning to the word worship. It does not limit it to praise meetings and liturgical worship. What does it say? Have you thought of worship in this way before? COMMENT.

LOOK AT Hebrews 12:28. The verse also speaks of 'acceptable worship'. Consider this verse in the context of the whole chapter. What does it tell you about offering to God 'acceptable worship, with reverence and awe?'

READ 1 Corinthians 11:23-32. The Communion (Eucharist or Lord's Supper) is the central act of liturgical worship in many churches. In this passage Paul not only emphasizes its importance, but also the need to consider seriously how one participates in the eating of the bread and drinking of the cup.

What does it mean to you to join with others around the Lord's table? THINK ABOUT THIS in prepraration for your group meeting.

What do you think it means to profane the body and blood of the Lord (v.27)? WRITE DOWN your answer to this.

SPACE IS PROVIDED BELOW FOR YOU TO WRITE DOWN THOUGHTS THAT COME TO YOU DURING THE WEEK AS YOU PRAY AND READ THE BIBLE.

How to Serve Together

SECTION 4 WEEK 4

POINT OF STUDY: Serving the Lord together is more than getting certain necessary jobs done. It is a matter of how one works together and to what end.

Study to be completed:

Read the following through several times. Take time to think about what you have read.
Answer the question put to you at the end.

Each member is committed to love the others and to give practical service to the body; that is, to the church or fellowship. Every Christian is called to do this. Often it is easier to serve than it is to love; this is why it is important not only to take up one's responsibilities, but also how one does it and to what end. There are certain principles which have to be taught and worked out.

A right attitude

'Whoever would be great among you must be your servant, and whoever would be first among you must be your slave' (Matthew 20:25-28). There must be no jockeying for position, no evading of responsibility. The desire of each must be to serve the whole body — not just serving one's own interests or the interests of a particular group.

To what end?

There is the need for everyone to keep clearly in the forefront of his thinking that vision which God gives of the body functioning to its fullest potential, giving life to all around. This comes through learning how to pray, study and worship together, but more than this it comes through a willingness to share oneself and one's life with others. Also there needs to be an appreciation of each person's place and function in the body and this includes a recognition of those God has called to lead and a willingness to support that leadership.

Working it out

It is important that those who pray, study and worship together are those who also serve together in practical ways. God gives direction to those who are willing to commit themselves to seeing a vision fulfilled.

God calls all kinds of people to serve him and it is in the working alongside others that people often rub each other up the wrong way. When this happens one's commitment to stay together in order to love and work through the problem is tested. It takes time to grow together and if a group of people do not stay together then God cannot fully work out his purposes for them.

Plan of action

'Where there is no vision the people perish' Proverbs 29:18a.

'Write the vision; make it plain upon tablets, so he may run who reads it...' Habakkuk 2:2. A vision can be thought of as a plan of action. What plan of action has God got for your church or fellowship? How do you see it?

WRITE DOWN YOUR THOUGHTS ABOUT THIS

Study questions

1

LOOK AT Matthew 6:24; Luke 12:35-40; Galatians 1:10; Colossians 3:22-24. What qualities do you need in your life in order to be able to serve God? WRITE your answer below.

READ Philippians 1:27; Ephesians 4:1-3,15,16. What qualities do you need in your life in order to be able to work alongside others in the body? WRITE your answer below.

2

LOOK AGAIN at Matthew 20:25-28. What is required of those who are called to lead others? See also 1 Peter 5:1-5.

READ Hebrews 13:17. What should be one's attitude to those in positions of leadership in the body of Christ?

LOOK AGAIN at 1 Peter 5:5. Who should clothe themselves 'with humility?'

If time, read Ephesians 5:21 – 6:9. Here Paul lays down principles of behaviour for different relationships in the body of Christ. But first he emphasizes the one overriding principle for peaceful relationships throughout the whole body. See verse 21. What do you learn from this?

FIND other verses in the New Testament which have something to say about leadership or eldership. What do you learn from these verses? SUMMARISE your findings below.

If time, read the letter of Paul to Philemon. In verse 16, Paul asks Onesimus to relate to Philemon as 'a beloved brother'. What does it mean for members of the body of Christ to relate to each other as brothers? CONSIDER this in the light of the study you have just completed on leadership.

SPACE IS PROVIDED BELOW FOR YOU TO WRITE DOWN THOUGHTS THAT COME TO YOU DURING THE WEEK AS YOU PRAY AND READ THE BIBLE.

Living Together

SECTION 5

How to Love One Another

SECTION 5 WEEK 1

POINT OF STUDY: 'Your strong love for each other will prove to the world that you are my disciples'. Jesus said this to his disciples; the same is true for us today. Learning how to love one another is a top priority for us as Christians.

Study to be completed:

Read the following through several times. Take time to think about what you have read. Answer the questions.

'A new commandment I give to you, that you love one another; even as I have loved you, that you also love one another. By this all men will know that you are my disciples, if you have love for one another' (John 13:34,35). Jesus knew what he was asking when he said to his friends, '...even as I have loved you...love one another'. He was challenging them to something deeper than 'love your neighbour as yourself'. Jesus had lived, worked and shared his life for three years with these same twelve men. He had been in their homes, seen them at their places of work, called them to follow him. He had known them as excitable Christian workers coming back from a successful mission – highly delighted with themselves – and been with them when they were quarrelling and squabbling. They were very changeable in their attitudes and actions; nevertheless, he kept on loving them. They knew the kind of love Jesus was requiring of them; he had demonstrated it to them.

Jesus knew even as he ate his last meal with them that within a matter of hours all would fail him. His concern, however, was not for himself, but for them. He knew about putting up with people's faults and failings, about forgiving seventy times seven. After Jesus rose from the dead he made a particular point of talking with Peter, the man who vowed he would never let him down and then, within twenty-four hours, went and did just that. Jesus let Peter know that he forgave him and at the same time entrusted him with the responsible task of caring for others.

There was one disciple who said of himself that he was 'the disciple whom Jesus loved' (John 13:23; 21:7). He and Jesus were very close friends. As far as he was able, John stayed near Jesus during his trial and crucifixion. Jesus' nickname for John as for his brother James, was 'son of thunder' (Mark 3:17). John must have changed greatly through his relationship with Jesus. He is the one who wrote, 'Dear friends, let us practice loving each other, for love comes from God and those who are loving and kind show that they are the children of God, and that they are getting to know him better. But if a person isn't loving and kind, it shows that he doesn't know God – for God is love' (1 John 4:7,8, *The Living Bible*). John's first epistle is full of teaching about the importance of loving each other.

Study questions:

1 Jesus and his friends

READ the following passages through slowly and thoughtfully. In what practical ways did Jesus demonstrate his love for his friends? CONSIDER this question as you read the passages. You may want to make notes as you go along, using some scrap paper for this purpose. At the end WRITE DOWN your answer to the question, picking out four ways which stand out to you.

Passages to look up:

Matthew 4:18-22; Mark 3:13-19; Matthew 12:46-50; Mark 9:30-37; Luke 22:1-62; John 13:1-17; 15:12-17, chapter 17; John 19:25-27; Mark 16:1-14; John chapters 20 and 21.

2

READ 1 John 3:10-24; 4:7-21; 5:1-3. Read these passages in two different translations. THINK ABOUT them. They are all about God's love for us and the love he requires us to have for each other. What do these verses say? WRITE DOWN your answer.

READ 2 Corinthians 6:11-13.

Paul felt that this relationship with the Christians in Corinth had in some way become rather tense and strained. For his part he wanted to remain completely open and loving with them. Consider his plea to the Corinthians that they respond to him in the same way.

If a person is 'restricted in their affections' (*The Living Bible* paraphrases this as 'your love is too small and does not reach out to me and draw me in') what can he or she do about it? What advice would you give to a person who has this problem? WRITE DOWN your answer.

USE THE SPACE BELOW TO TAKE NOTES OF THE RECORDED TALK TO BE PLAYED AT THE GROUP MEETING

There are four recorded talks which you will be listening to as part of this section of the course. One will be played each week for the next four weeks. Taking notes as you listen is an aid to concentration — and to remembering.

If you are not used to taking notes in this way you may want to use a piece of scrap paper as you listen and then add your notes to your book later.

How to Encourage One Another

SECTION 5 WEEK 2

POINT OF STUDY: 'Therefore encourage one another and build one another up, just as you are doing' (1 Thessalonians 5:11). There are times when each of us needs encouragement. As members one of another we should be seeking to know how best to receive and give encouragement.

Study to be completed:

Read the following through several times. Take time to think about what you have read. Answer the questions.

'For I long to see you, that I may impart to you some spiritual gift to strengthen you, that is, that we may be mutually encouraged by each other's faith, both yours and mine' (Romans 1:11,12).

Paul, who wrote these words to the Romans, was the man who also wrote to the Corinthians that he had had more imprisonments than any; had had countless beatings and had often been near death. He had also been cold, hungry and thirsty, and had many times been stoned and in danger. In all this he had learnt the value of encouraging others and also the importance of being encouraged himself. Paul knew that if he let these calamities get on top of him then he could be of no help or encouragement to others.

God was to Paul the source of every consolation and comfort and encouragement; the one who encouraged him in every trouble, calamity and affliction. He was, therefore, able to encourage others with the same encouragement that God gave to him. On one occasion he was in such distress, so unbearably crushed, that he despaired of life itself, but God rescued him. The Christians Paul was writing to were praying for him; he knew that his deliverance was a result of their prayers, that they had shared with him in his sufferings and also in the encouragement that was his through Christ. See 2 Corinthians 1:3-11, *Amplified Bible.*

Paul was never so strong and self-sufficient that he did not need the encouragement and friendship of others. Time and again in his epistles we see glimpses of just how much he needed his friends and how he looked to them for support and encouragement. 'Is there any such thing as Christians cheering each other up? Do you love me enough to want to help me? Does it mean anything to you that we are brothers in the Lord, sharing the same Spirit? Are your hearts tender and sympathetic at all? Then make me truly happy by loving each other and agreeing wholeheartedly with each other, working together with one heart and mind and purpose' (Philippians 2:1,2, *The Living Bible*).

Learning how to receive encouragement is the secret of being able to encourage others. Both are necessary.

To encourage means to 'make bold, put heart into'. The word is derived from a Latin word meaning 'heart', the seat of intelligence or of feeling. It is that state of mind which enables one to encounter danger or difficulties with firmness, or without fear or fainting of heart.

Study questions:

1

The need for encouragement is often related to a specific difficulty or time of discouragement. Note the following passages which relate to encouragement. Against each verse of group of verses DESCRIBE briefly (a) the specific difficulty or discouragement referred to, (b) the kind of encouragement, or promise of encouragement given. An example is given of the type of answer required.

Genesis 26:24 (see vv. 12-33 for context)

SAMPLE ANSWER: The people were jealous of Isaac's prosperity and made life difficult for him. In the midst of these difficulties God appeared to him and told him not to be afraid for he was with him and would bless him. In the end the differences between Isaac and his neighbours were settled peaceably.

Exodus 14:13 (see vv. 10-18 for context)

Isaiah 43:1, 2

Isaiah 49:14-16

Matthew 14:27 (see vv. 22-23 for context)

John 14:18-20

Acts 23:11 (see 22:30 and 23:1-15 for context)

Revelation 1:17,18 (see vv. 12-19 for context)

2

THINK of times when God had similarly encouraged you. WRITE briefly the details of two such times in your life, stating what the situation was and how God encouraged you.

③

In Romans 1:12 Paul speaks of being 'mutually strengthened and encouraged by each other's faith, both yours and mine'. The following excerpts from the story of David and Johnathan illustrate this type of mutual encouragement. READ the passages. What do you learn from them? WRITE OUT your answer.

1 Samuel 18:1-4 (see also 17:31-58 for context); 19:1-7; 20:1-42; 22:7,8; 23:15-18; 2 Samuel 1:17-27; 9:1-13.

USE THE SPACE BELOW TO TAKE NOTES OF THE RECORDED TALK TO BE PLAYED AT THE GROUP MEETING.

How to Serve One Another

SECTION 5 WEEK 3

POINT OF STUDY: Jesus said he came to be among men 'as one who serves'. If we are expressing his life we will be seeking to follow his example in this as in other things.

Study to be completed:

As an introduction to this week's study answer the following two questions:

1

What do you think it means to be 'as one who serves'?

2

What things hinder us from serving others?

Turn back to Section 4, Week 4. Read again the study on 'How to Serve Together', noting the answers you gave then.

Now read the following through several times. Take time to think about what you have read. Answer the questions.

'A dispute also arose among them, which of them was to be regarded as the greatest. And he said to them, "The Kings of the Gentiles exercise lordship over them; and those in authority over them are called benefactors. But not so with you; rather let the greatest among you become as the youngest, and the leader as one who serves. For which is the greater, one who sits at table, or one who serves? Is it not the one who sits at table? But I am among you as one who serves" ' (Luke 22:24-27).

Jesus came to live among men as a servant. Paul wrote concerning him '...who, though he was in the form of God, did not count equality with God a thing to be grasped, but emptied himself, taking the form of a servant...' (Philippians 2:6,7a). His service began with those closest to him — his friends. This is where it usually hits hardest. To be told what to do by one's boss and to do it is comparatively easy compared to anticipating the needs of one's friends and working to meet those needs. But this is what Jesus did. He took responsibility for the twelve men who were his constant companions and saw that their needs were met. He expected the same of them and had at times to rebuke them for their failure to anticipate and meet his needs.

Service to one another is a two way thing. We all serve one another. No one is exempt. We are called to learn how to lay down our lives for one another (1 John 3:16). Many Christian workers are willing to lay down their lives for the world, but have never learnt how to do it for their brothers and sisters in the body of Christ. This, however, is the practical outworking of our love for one another and the demonstration to the world that we are disciples of Jesus Christ.

Like his Lord and Master, Paul served the needs of those around him and of those who travelled with him. He in his turn received service from them. He could not have accomplished the task entrusted to him by God without the willing help and service of his friends. See 1 Thessalonians 2:7-9; 2 Thessalonians 3:7-10; Acts 20:34,35; 2 Corinthians 11:28,19; Romans 16:3,4; 1 Corinthians 16:17,18; Philippians 2:25-30; 2 Timothy 4:11-13. There are those who find it easier to serve others than to let others serve them. It is necessary to both give and receive service. In this way we demonstrate our willingness to open up our lives to one another, to consider the interests of others not only our own.

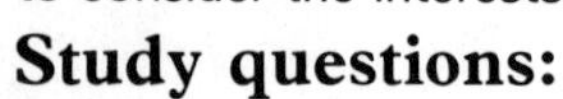

Study questions:

1

The following verses deal with various aspects of our service to God. Against each verse NOTE DOWN what they say. Consider whether these same things apply in relation to our serving one another.

Joshua 24:15

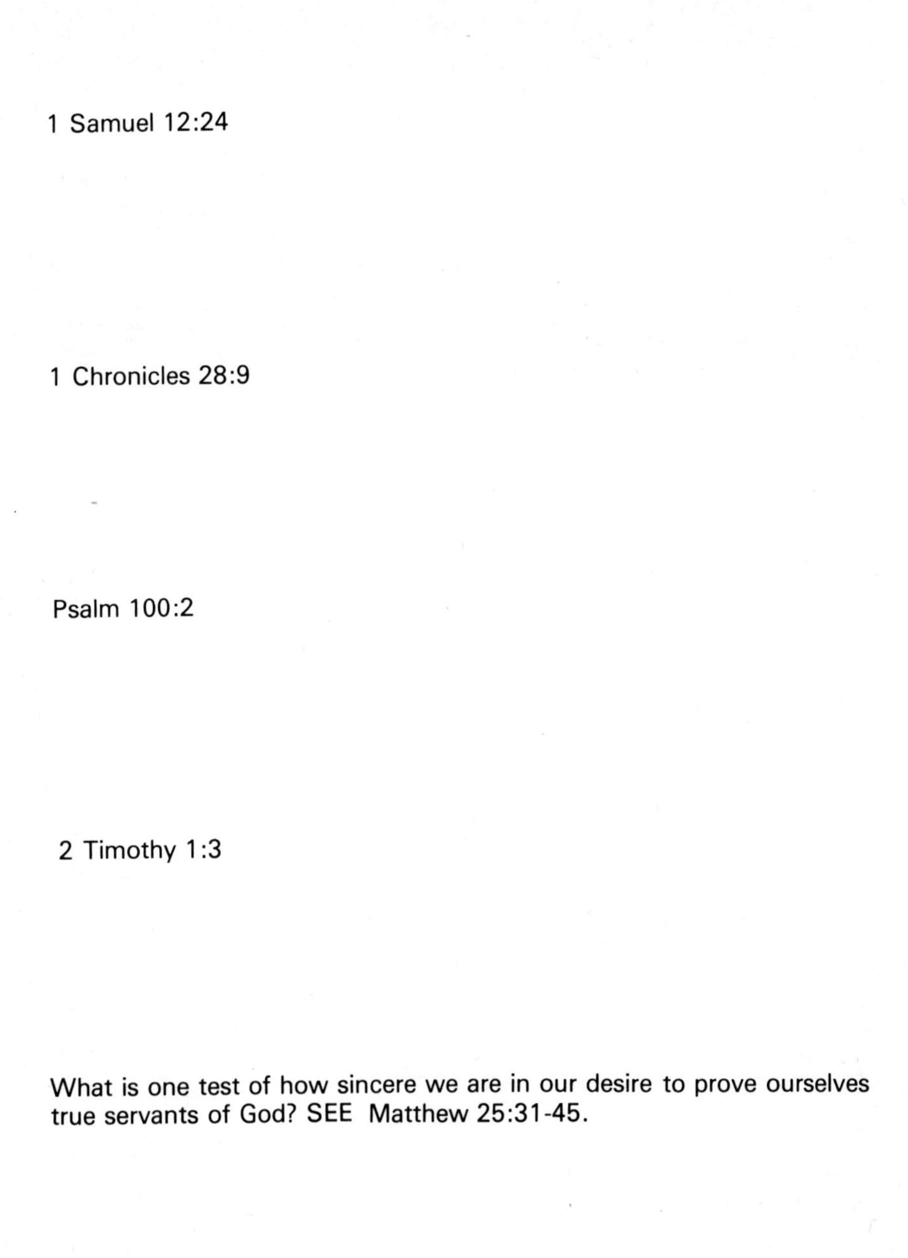

1 Samuel 12:24

1 Chronicles 28:9

Psalm 100:2

2 Timothy 1:3

What is one test of how sincere we are in our desire to prove ourselves true servants of God? SEE Matthew 25:31-45.

2

READ the account in John 13:1-17 of Jesus washing the disciples' feet. This was the menial task of a servant in those days. Would you do this for anyone in your group? Would you allow any of them to do it for you? What equivalent job can you think of that would be parallel to it today? THINK ABOUT these questions.

ANSWER the following two questions:

What lesson do you think Jesus was attempting to teach here?

What application, if any, has it got for us today?

If possible, read the commentary on this passage in *Readings in St. John's Gospel* by William Temple. Turn to any other commentaries you have to hand and see what they have to say about this passage.

Martha is seemingly an outstanding example of 'one who serves'. It was Mary, however, who gained Jesus' commendation. READ the account in Luke 10:38-42. What was Martha doing wrong that she gained such a rebuke from Jesus? Are there dangers inherent in serving others? If so, what are they? What are the balancing factors? WRITE as full an answer as you can to the above questions drawing on your own experience and, if time allows, digging deeper into what the bible has to say about the matter.

USE THE SPACE BELOW TO TAKE NOTES OF THE RECORDED TALK TO BE PLAYED AT THE GROUP MEETING.

How to Trust One Another

SECTION 5 WEEK 4

POINT OF STUDY: As members of the body of Christ we are called to share together in openness and trust; like the apostle Paul to share not only the gospel but to share our lives with one another (1 Thessalonians 2:8).

Study to be completed:

Read the following through several times. Take time to think about what you have read. Answer the questions.

Lack of trust in one another causes us to put up barriers and never fully to take our place in the body and to fulfil our calling or ministry. Some are stunted in their growth because they feel that others in the fellowship do not trust them. It is the reason why so many misunderstandings between people are never cleared up. To learn to trust each other is often the first step to experiencing a deeper fellowship.

At the commencement of his ministry Jesus chose twelve men to be with him constantly. At the end of three years he knew that he would have to entrust to them the continuation of his work on earth. Jesus' trust in the power of his Father to change these men, and his trust in them that they would respond, made it possible for him to continue to share his life with them long after we would have given up.

As he was preparing to leave them to carry on his work, he told them about the Holy Spirit, who was to be their comforter, counsellor, helper, intercessor, advocate, strengthener and standby. See John 14:26 in the Amplified Bible. We all have the same Spirit within us. As we take time to hear the Holy Spirit in one another we will grow to a deeper understanding and trust of each other. We will come more quickly to see the fruit of the Spirit in action in one another and rejoice in the constancy of his work in changing each of us into the likeness of Jesus Christ.

We need to be in a constant state of forgiving one another so that the Holy Spirit isn't grieved and that no root of bitterness is allowed to spring up in our midst. We need to be able to speak the truth to one another, but this is only possible as we take time and effort to build up good, loving relationships in order that the truth can be spoken without unnecessary hurt. Knowing we are loved and accepted by others sets us free to be ourselves. As this happens, so we are able to expose parts of ourselves instead of hiding behind a front that may have been built up over the years to cover hurts, rejections and inferiority feelings. As we are able to be exposed to one another in a loving, forgiving fellowship so we can learn to trust one another. James 5:16 says, 'Therefore confess your sins to one another, and pray for one another, that you may be healed'. As we confess our faults to one another and cover them with love and prayer, a deep love and trust for one another emerges in the body.

Study questions

1

Why do we often find it so difficult to trust one another? THINK ABOUT this. WRITE OUT your answer.

2

It is said of Jesus that he did not trust himself to certain people. SEE John 2:23-25. The Authorised Version translates this as he '...did not commit himself unto them...'. He did, however, make himself very vulnerable to those who were his constant companions; he did commit himself to them. We are called to trust God without reservation. How important is it, do you consider, that we trust each other as brothers and sisters in the body of Christ? Are there balancing factors here? Are there some people we should be careful of trusting too much? WRITE DOWN your thoughts.

③

The book of Ephesians has a lot to say about the church and about how we should be behaving towards one another as Christians. READ the book through twice — in two different translations — studying it from both these angles. SUMMARISE what you have learnt. If there is no time to complete this question now, return to it and complete it later.

USE THE SPACE BELOW TO TAKE NOTES OF THE RECORDED TALK TO BE PLAYED AT THE GROUP MEETING.

Expressing the Life of Christ

SECTION 6

Introduction

This is the last section of the course, but we trust the beginning of something new for you as a church or fellowship. It may be that this course has opened up new possibilities for you as an individual and for you corporately as a group. It may be that through it God has been consolidating many things you had already begun to work out in your own life and in the fellowship. Either way, it is what follows after you have completed this course which will determine how much benefit it has been to you. You need to be praying that the Holy Spirit will be directing you as to the next steps you need to take, so that you continue to work out the things you have been learning.

Suppose you began to see your prayers for your church or fellowship really being answered in a very definite way? How ready would you be for the consequences? Quite likely you are already experiencing renewal in the life of your fellowship and already know something about the consequences. When the Holy Spirit begins to renew the life of a church then inevitably things have to change to accommodate the many needs and opportunities that arise. God is renewing his church, and there are certain steps you can begin to take in order that you may experience more fully this work of renewal. There is, however, a cost involved — for renewal involves change.

You are the body of Christ called to express his forgiveness, his faith, his love, his life. What does this mean in practice? This is the question you need to be considering this month. At the end of each week's study we will suggest you note down POINTS I NEED TO CONSIDER MORE CAREFULLY AND TO PRAY ABOUT and POINTS I WOULD LIKE US TO DISCUSS AT OUR GROUP MEETING.

There are only a few study questions to answer. This is to give you time to review some of the things you learnt earlier in the course. In Week 4 we give you space to sum up what you feel you have learnt.

Expressing His Forgiveness

SECTION 6 WEEK 1

POINT OF STUDY: In all our encounters with people we are to express God's love for them, his offer of forgiveness and new life.

Study to be completed:

Read the following through several times. Take time to think about what you have read. Answer the study question.

'And Jesus went about all the cities and villages, teaching in their synagogues and preaching the gospel of the kingdom, and healing every disease and every infirmity. When he saw the crowds, he had compassion for them, because they were harassed and helpless, like sheep without a shepherd' (Matthew 9:35,36).

Jesus gave himself for others because he had this tremendous compassion which motivated him to care, to love and finally to die. In saying this one needs to remember that Jesus also took time aside to pray and to be quiet and he spent much of his time with just a few people teaching and sharing with them. Part of the way he taught his disciples was to take them with him into the streets and into homes where he spent time with 'the wrong people', whom he was criticised for befriending.

Wherever he went he made friends. Perhaps we have not understood the full implication of the fact that Jesus was called 'the friend of publicans and sinners' (Matthew 11:19; Luke 7:34). How many do we count among our friends who are such? We need to be mingling with people, making friends with them so that they can get to know us and discover what faith in Jesus means to us.

People need to know us as we really are — not with our 'religious shields' up; they will then discover how real Jesus Christ is to us. It is more than taking every opportunity to speak about Jesus, it is allowing him to express himself through us in very natural and open ways. This means learning to open ourselves to others, letting them get close enough to us so that they can really get to know us. The place to begin to do this is with a group of committed people within the fellowship, but it does not end there. Let people see us as we really are and they will be able to see Christ in us.

Outsiders coming into our churches and fellowships should sense immediately that they are coming face to face with people who know a lot about living, loving and forgiving — real people, not 'religious people'; those who, knowing their faults and weaknesses, have nevertheless discovered they are loved by God and who, in opening themselves to his love, are being changed by it. As we become such people, so we will be able to reach out to others in the same way that Jesus did in love and forgiveness.

Study question:

CONSIDER Jesus in the following encounters he had with people. USE YOUR IMAGINATION as you read these passages. How do you think these people felt? What effect did Jesus have on them? From these passages what do you learn about Jesus and of the way he related to people? WRITE OUT your answer.

Matthew 9:9-13; Luke 7:36-50; John 4:1-42; 8:1-11.

POINTS I NEED TO CONSIDER MORE CAREFULLY AND TO PRAY ABOUT:

POINTS I WOULD LIKE US TO DISCUSS AT OUR GROUP MEETING:

Review

Read Sections 1 and 2 again.

Recall the impression these sections made on you,
any questions they raised,
any way in which they challenged you.

Consider whether you have been aware of any change(s) in your life as a result.
whether you have thought any more about the issues raised.
whether you have gained any fresh understanding of these matters since completing your study.
whether you would change any of your answers.

Use some scrap paper for writing down thoughts which you have. This will help you when you come to complete your summary of the whole course later on in this section.

Expressing His Faith

SECTION 6 WEEK 2

POINT OF STUDY: As individuals our faith may sometimes be small, but a group of people encouraging and supporting each other, building one another up in the faith, will grow strong in faith – for their own needs and for the needs of others.

Study to be completed:

Read the following through several times. Take time to think about what you have read. Answer the study questions.

Faith is God's gift to us, one which needs to be treasured and which we need to guard carefully, so that it is being added to, not knocked away. Often there will be those in a church or fellowship whose faith is stronger than that of others and the Holy Spirit often uses such people to bring about a greater measure of belief and expectancy in the rest of the body. Where this faith is springing forth it is important to

encourage it and to direct it, not to allow it to be undermined by those who find it less easy to believe. Those who find it hard to have faith are not to be made to feel condemned; they are to be encouraged to use the faith they have. Jesus said that a little faith can move a mountain.

Where a group of people have been drawn together by the Holy Spirit they should expect God to give them a vision of what he wants to do through them. He will speak through circumstances, through the word of God, through the gifts of the Spirit, and he will make a strong impression upon several that he is wanting to establish a particular work through that church or fellowship. Some will have faith to believe for this, others at first will be hesitant and uncertain.

The Holy Spirit will begin to show initial steps which need to be taken and it is as these are taken that faith will begin to flower openly in the body. As a result, people's lives will be changed, the sick will be healed,. people will be drawn to put their trust in Christ. Difficulties and problems will also arise to test this faith and firm, wise leadership will be needed.

Turn back to page123.What did you write in answer to the question, 'What plan of action has God got for your fellowship?' Would you change or add to what you wrote then? Do you expect to see this plan accomplished? In the Old Testament we read of the Israelites who drifted for forty years never taking hold of the land that God had promised them because they did not believe God enough to act on his word to them. They spent most of their time grumbling about the hard time they were having — blaming God when they should have been facing up to the fact that they themselves were to blame. They should have been pressing on into the land that God had promised; everything they complained they lacked, awaited them there.

As a church or fellowship you need *to act* in faith for faith to grow.

Study questions:

1

READ through 1 and 2 Thessalonians. With the help of a concordance and any commentaries discover as much as you can about the church at Thessalonica. SUMMARISE what you have learnt. In his two letters to the Thessalonians what does Paul have to say about (a) their faith and (b) their love for one another? MAKE A NOTE of these things. NOTE below any points you find particularly challenging.

2

Timothy was a close friend, companion and confidant of Paul. Paul looked upon him as a son; someone on whom he could unquestionably rely (Philippians 2:19-22). It would seem, however, that Timothy was of a somewhat nervous disposition and had often to be encouraged by Paul not to write himself down. It was important to Paul that Timothy took care not to allow his faith, or the faith of others, to be undermined by people or circumstances. READ 1 Timothy 1:1-7; 18-20; 6:3-10,20,21; 2 Timothy 2:10-19. What do you learn from these passages? What are some of the things Paul mentioned as likely to undermine one's faith? Can you think of other ways by which faith can be undermined?

POINTS I NEED TO CONSIDER MORE CAREFULLY AND PRAY ABOUT:

POINTS I WOULD LIKE US TO DISCUSS AT OUR GROUP MEETING:

Review

Read Section 3 again

Recall the impression it made on you,
any questions it raised,
any way in which it challenged you.

Consider whether you have been aware of any change(s) in your life as a result,
whether you have thought any more about the issues raised,
whether you have gained any fresh understanding of these matters since completing your study,
whether you would change any of your answers.

Use some scrap paper for writing down any thoughts which you have. This will help you when you come to complete your summary of the whole course later on in this section.

Expressing His Love

SECTION 6 WEEK 3

POINT OF STUDY: Christ's love needs to be experienced and communicated in practical ways. To express his love will often mean we have to sacrifice something we hold dear.

Study to be completed:

Read the following through several times. Take time to think about what you have read. Answer the study question.

'The work at Post Green started as a result of what God did for us. He showed us a new dimension of loving — deeper, far deeper, than normal human relationships. More vulnerable, completely open, not condemning in any way, forgiving and therefore healing. He not only gave us his love for others, but gave us a longing to teach this love to others'. This is how Tom Lees describes the start of the work which has grown up around his home in Dorset, England.

The love that we experience as we are renewed by the Holy Spirit warms and encourages us. Through this experience we discover more about Jesus; we begin to understand what motivated him, how he felt about his Father and about people. We begin to understand what it was that compelled Paul to endure such hardships for the gospel's sake. What began at Post Green through such an experience demanded even more as time went on. Love does make a high demand upon us. It may ask us to be willing to open our homes to others in such a way that it is no longer 'our home'. It may require us to become less possessive in our relationships, to be willing to change our style of living, to share not only ourselves but also our material possessions with others.

God is asking his people to make such changes. For many, renewal is upsetting their manner of living and the structures they are used to in home and church. Why is God doing this? He is doing it because room is needed in our lives for what God wants to do in the reshaping of his church. We need to make room for others so that they can know they are truly included — part of a family, the family of God.

The way renewal comes about and the form it takes will vary from place to place, but wherever the Spirit is allowed to bring new life it will mean change and will cost everyone something he holds dear. Unless those who are praying, believing and working for renewal are also saying, 'Lord, I am willing, whatever the cost' it may never come, or if it comes it may never be fully implemented.

As people come into contact with our churches and fellowships they need to be able to feel the love. There came the time at Post Green when people began to say, 'What has happened to the love?'. It was not that there was less love but that there were more people — too many to be loved in the same way by just one family and a few other people. It began to be apparent that what was needed was a community into which many people could fit, and where they could experience real love and care. A lot can happen from just one family willing to open up its home to others.

Study questions

Paul ended most of his letters by listing all the people he wanted to be remembered to or had a personal message for. People were important to Paul — he had a very deep love for many. READ slowly and thoughtfully through the following passages:
Romans 16:1-23; 1 Corinthians 16:10-20; Ephesians 6:21,22; Philippians 4:18-22; Colossians 4:7-17; 2 Timothy 4:9-22; Philemon. On a bit of scrap paper NOTE down the things that strike you. Paul could never have accomplished alone what God had called him to do, he was dependent upon many others playing their part. As you read CONSIDER the two questions put to you in (b).

a. SUMMARISE your feelings and thoughts about the passages you have read.

b. Do you think Paul was an easy man to work with? How do you think he managed to keep the love and support of so many people and what lessons do you think he personally had to learn in order to do this? WRITE DOWN your thoughts about this.

POINTS I NEED TO CONSIDER MORE CAREFULLY AND TO PRAY ABOUT:

POINTS I WOULD LIKE US TO DISCUSS AT OUR GROUP MEETING:

Review

Read	Sections 4 and 5 again.
Recall	the impression these sections made on you, any questions they raised any way in which they challenged you.
Consider	whether you have been aware of any change(s) in your life as a result, whether you have gained any fresh understanding of these matters since completing your study. whether you would change any of your answers.

Use some scrap of paper for writing down thoughts which you have. This will help you when you come to complete your summary of the whole course later on in this section.

Expressing His Life

SECTION 6 WEEK 4

POINT OF STUDY: For a church or fellowship to express Christ's life fully calls for a deep commitment from everyone involved. It involves a commitment to God and to one another – that is, a common agreement to live out Christ's life and to follow the leading of the Holy Spirit.

Study to be completed:

1 A place for God among his people, as symbolised in the Old Testament

READ the following passages: (a) The building of the tabernacle. Exodus 25:1-9; 35:4-35; 36:1-7. (b) The building of the temple. 1 Chronicles 28:9-21; 29:1-9.

What kind of challenge was put to the people in the above instances? How did they respond? What do you think caused this response from them? GIVE your answers below:

2 A place for God among his people, as revealed in the New Testament

READ the following passages: 1 Peter 2:4-10; Ephesians 2:19-22; 4:1-16.

What kind of building is spoken about in these passages? What are the bricks that go into the making of this building? Is the response required of us more or less than that of the people involved in the building of the tabernacle and of the temple? To what end is this building being formed? GIVE your answers below:

Read the following through several times. Take time to think about what you have read. Complete the final assignments.

'Now you are the body of Christ and individually members of it' (1 Corinthians 11:27).

Every member of the body of Christ is important to its functioning properly. Each person must be aware of his place in the body, not seeing his contribution in isolation to what others are doing.

Also for a fellowship to grow strong and to become an expression of Christ's life to those around — to be continually renewed in its life and ministry — there will need to be at least some people ('a core group' of ordained and lay members) who are committed to seeing this happen. For such renewal will not come about overnight, and it will not happen without the dedication and consistency of such a core group. For some this will mean facing up to the challenge that their place and position in the local church may need to take precedence over the demands of job, career, etc.

The kind of commitment we have talked about in this study will mean different things to different people and groups. But for all concerned it will mean, first and foremost, a commitment to love one another; to work towards a common aim and purpose; to meet together regularly; to share one's life — including a willingness to share one's home and possessions, as God may direct. It will mean not giving up when things get difficult, not hiving off when one is offended in any way, not evading responsibilities because it is more comfortable or convenient to do so. It will mean helping one another in love to work out this commitment to express Christ's life.

POINTS I NEED TO CONSIDER MORE CAREFULLY AND TO PRAY ABOUT:

POINTS I WOULD LIKE US TO DISCUSS AT OUR GROUP MEETING

Review

Consider prayerfully and carefully what God has been saying to you through this whole course and, in particular, through this last section (Section 6).

Look back over the notes you have made as you have reviewed the other sections in the course. SUM UP your thoughts in the space below.

COMPLETE THIS LAST QUESTION AT YOUR GROUP MEETING

What steps are you agreed you need to take *now* to be working towards the vision God has given you for your church or fellowship?